Trog makes a trap

by Ben Butterworth
pictures by Lorraine Calaora

Nelson

2

Trog was hungry.
Father was hungry.

Mother was hungry.
Grandpa Gripe was **very** hungry.

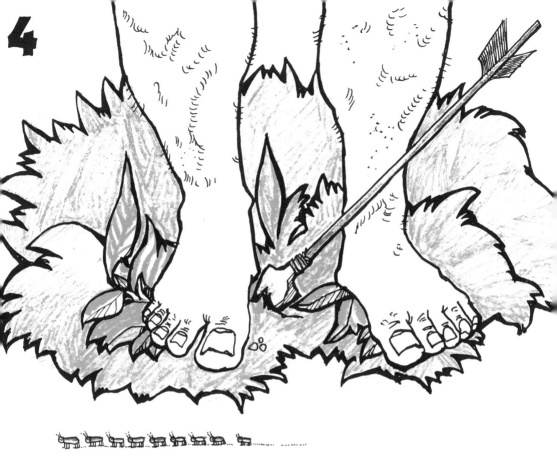

Father and Trog had been hunting
with bows and arrows.
Father had not shot anything.
Trog had nearly shot something.
He had nearly shot Father
in the foot.

Grandpa Gripe and Trog
had been hunting with their spears.
Trog had not speared anything.
Grandpa Gripe
had nearly speared something.
He had nearly speared Trog.

'The Quickerwits
are never hungry,' Mother said.
'They catch lots of animals.
Trog, go and find out what they do.'

'Right, I will,'
Trog said to his mother.

Trog went over the hills,
over the rivers,
to the land of the Quickerwits.

'How do you catch animals?
How do you hunt?' he asked them.

'It's easy,' the Quickerwits said.
'We find a path the animals go along
and make a deep pit there.

8

We cover the pit with sticks
and we go and hide.
The animals do not see the pit
and they fall in.
Then they cannot get out.
It's a good trap.'

'No bows and arrows?' Trog asked.
'No spears?'

'That's right,' the Quickerwits said.
'No bows and arrows and no spears.'

'Good,' Trog said.

Trog went back over the hills,
over the rivers to Mother,
Father and Grandpa Gripe.
'It's easy,' he said.
'I will make a pit.
It will trap the animals for us.'

'rog went with Father to the woods.
Ie found a path and made a deep pit.
Ie covered it with sticks
nd hid with Father.

Something came along the path.

Then –

Something was in the pit.
Trog and Father ran to look.

14

It was Grandpa Gripe!

'Wait till I get that boy!'
yelled Grandpa.
'Wait till I get out of this pit.'

'I'm not waiting,' Trog said.
He ran off, as fast as he could
to the land of the Quickerwits.

'Did you make a pit?'
the Quickerwits asked him.

'I did,' Trog said.

'Did you trap anything?' they asked

'Oh yes,' Trog said,
'I trapped something.
It was Grandpa Gripe.'

أفكار واقتراحات

الأهداف:

* التعرّف على مبادئ إيقاع اللغة.
* قراءة كلمات تامّة.
* الانتباه إلى تشابه الكلمتين في الحرف الأوّل الّذي تبدأ به كلّ منهما (ك، ش، ف، ن، ج، م، ه).
* الانتباه إلى التشابه بين أصوات الحرف الأوّل في الكلمتين.
* التعرّف على "و" كحرف عطف.

روابط مع الموادّ التعليميّة ذات الصلة:

* مبادئ التهجئة.
* مبادئ التعبير بالحركة.
* مبادئ الرسم والتلوين.

عدد الكلمات: ١٤

الأدوات: لوح أبيض، ورق، أقلام الرسم والتلوين

قبل القراءة:

* ماذا ترون على الغلاف؟ هيّا نقرأ العنوان معًا.
* ماذا يفعل هذا الصبيّ؟ هل يبدو سعيدًا؟ لِمَ هو سعيد يا ترى؟
* هل للحروف أصوات؟ ما هو صوت أوّل حرف في كلمة "كتاب"؟ وآخِر حرف؟

أثناء القراءة:

* أوّلاً، سنقرأ الكتاب معًا، ونشير إلى الكلمات.
* انتبهوا إلى التشابه في أشكال الحروف الأولى.
* انتبهوا إلى الفرق بين نطق "الضمّة" ونطق "الكسرة" في: "كُرَة" / "كِتاب".

كُرَة وَكِتاب

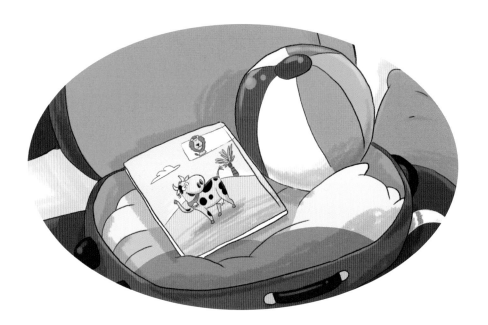

إعْداد: محمود جعفر وجاين ويتيك

بِريشة: جاريث كونواي

Collins

كُرَة

كِتَاب

كُرَة وَكِتاب

شَمْس

شَجَر

شَمْس وَشَجَر

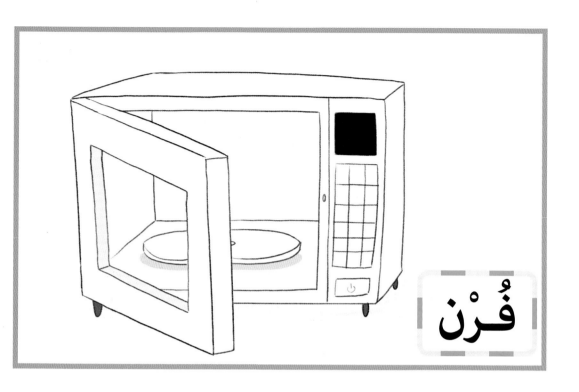

فُرْن

فُشار

فُرْن وَفُشار

نَخيل

نَجيل

نَخيل وَنَجيل

جَرّار

جَاروف

جَرّار وَجاروف

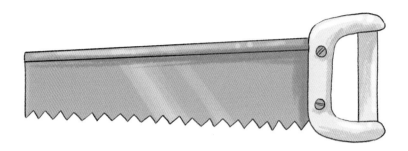

مِنْشار

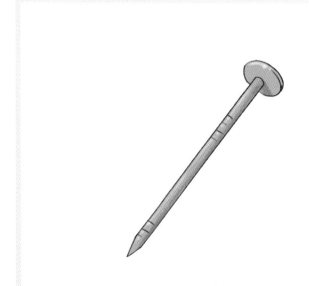

مِسْمار

مِنْشار وَمِسْمار

هُدْهُد

هَاتِف

هُدْهُد وَهاتِف!